Huntington Library Publications

CATALOGUE OF
WILLIAM BLAKE'S
DRAWINGS AND
PAINTINGS

in the Huntington Library

By

C. H. COLLINS BAKER

San Marino, California : 1938

Introduction

THE HUNTINGTON LIBRARY collection of original paintings and drawings by William Blake falls simply in groups: those done in water color, those in line alone, and those in an oil medium. Within these medium-groups other groups are defined according to subject. The chief part of the Huntington collection is three Miltonic sets, illustrating *Paradise Lost*, a hymn "On the Morning of Christ's Nativity," and *Comus*. These come in this catalogue. They are followed by separate water colors and drawings, including some of the so-called visionary portraits, and by the two oil-medium works in the collection. In a brief appendix are given a few drawings not by Blake, which were formerly attributed to him. Of these, two are by identified artists—Henry Pierce Bone and Henry Fuseli. Three have been grouped tentatively as "in the manner of Fuseli"; the initials "W. B." occur on two of them, and on two of them a false Blake signature has been added. On another of these dubious drawings an original monogram, apparently "A. W.," has been altered to "W. B." This group ends with two drawings, apparently Italian, which bear no resemblance to Blake's work.

Blake completed two, and may have contemplated more, sets of illustrations to *Paradise Lost*. The Huntington Library series, of 1807, is earlier than the other set, at Boston, and comprises twelve illustrations (plus one large duplicate), as against the nine at Boston. Being earlier it is more spontaneous in feeling, and lighter and freer in touch than the larger, elaborated drawings in the Boston series.

It was published in color by the Lyceum Press, Liverpool, in 1906, the year in which, under dual ownership, it was last seen publicly in England, at the Carfax Exhibition in London. The set was not again exhibited until 1936, then reunited in one ownership after half a century's separation.

Blake made two sets also of his six illustrations to the hymn on the Nativity. Here, again, the Huntington Library is fortunate in owning the earlier (*ca.* 1808), which was conceived by Blake in iridescent color, whereas the second set, now at Manchester, was drawn virtually in monochrome with strong pen outline.

The Huntington Library illustrations were reproduced in the Nonesuch Press "Milton" in 1926; they were last seen publicly in England, at auction, in 1912. Since then they have been once exhibited, in 1919, in New York.

Of his *Comus* drawings (the third series of Miltonic illustrations in the Huntington Library), two sets, again, were made by Blake. The other, and smaller, at Boston, differs largely in style, design, and detail from the Huntington version (*ca.* 1801), which Geoffrey Keynes regards as the earlier—rightly, if the tendency in the Boston series to reduce the heads, attenuate the forms, and generalize the anatomy be compared with the carefully solid construction of the figures in the Huntington drawings and the touching naïveté and intensity of their expressions.

These drawings were published in the Nonesuch Press "Milton" in 1926. They were last seen at an exhibition in England in 1914, and one in New York in 1919.

Two drawings unassociated with a series are in the Huntington collection. "The Hiding of Moses," which was engraved by Blake himself in 1825, probably from a considerably earlier drawing, is of peculiar beauty, associating itself in our minds with the spirit that animates his "Famine," produced about 1805.

This drawing was published by Keynes in his *Bibliography* in 1921. It had been seen in London at the sale of the Linnell Blake collection in 1918, probably its only public appearance.

The other unattached drawing is "The Conversion of Saul," probably the earliest work by Blake in the Library. So far as one can tell, this drawing had been lost to sight for more than half a century, having found its way into an extra-illustrated Bible of some fifty volumes. It has never been published before.

Blake's pencil drawings in the Huntington collection consist of one Dante subject, "Agnolo Brunelleschi and the Six-Footed Serpent," which was one of the seven Dante designs that Blake engraved. The rest of these line drawings are examples of academic rather than artistic interest. They represent Blake's unconvincing, and one might say uninspired, traffic in visionary portraiture. As evidence in support of his mystic communion with spirits, they seem negligible.

The two oil-medium works by Blake in the collection are not of great importance. "Lot and His Daughters" is not among Blake's most interesting experiments in this style, and the copy in oil of a figure from Michelangelo's "Last Judgment" is interesting only as an example of Blake's studentship.

Thus it will be seen that the chief part of the Huntington Library collection of Blakes consists of work produced between about 1798 and about 1808—that fruitful and comparatively placid period—and includes three series of Miltonic drawings to which Blake attached so much importance that he duplicated them. These drawings, never widely known, have, in the fluxion of time, dropped almost from ken; and when, a quarter of a century ago, they receded beyond the far western horizon they nearly faded from the sight of even the closest Blake students. The Trustees of the Huntington Library hope that this publication of these Blakes in California will be of service to those to whom so important a part of the master's Miltonic inspiration is of vital interest.

The titles of reference are given in full the first time they occur in the bibliographical notes, if they appear there: otherwise they are supplied at their first mention in the text. It is hardly necessary to explain here that when "Gilchrist" or "Keynes" is cited thus shortly, the book indicated is, in the one case, Alexander Gilchrist's *Life of William Blake* (London, 1863 and 1880), or, in the other, Geoffrey L. Keynes's *Bibliography of William Blake* (New York, 1921).

C. H. C. B.

Catalogue of William Blake's
Drawings and Paintings

WATER-COLOR DRAWINGS

Thirteen Illustrations to Milton's
"Paradise Lost" (1807)

I *Satan Calling His Legions* (PLATE I)

S ATAN stands on the beach of the Burning Lake, his arms aloft
in summons. Below him crouched, prone and seated, some
in gyves, his awakening host; on left and right some spring upward. Behind Satan a sleeping angel reclines, with back turned,
in the pose of a River God or of Theseus. Rusty-black cloud
forms in the upper corners, pale-red flames among the rocks and
figures. *Signed:* "18[--] W B[----]." [The edge has been cut.]
9 7/8 x 8 5/16 inches.

SEE *Paradise Lost*, I, 300, etc. It is evident that in composing this group
Blake's mind was running on Michelangelo's "Last Judgment" in the Sistine Chapel, engravings of which he had long studied. The seated angel,
behind Satan, generally recalling the Ilissos or the Theseus of the Parthenon
Pediments, is probably an adaptation of one of Michelangelo's Sistine fres-
coes—e. g., in the "Creation of the Sun and Moon"—or a reminiscence of
a figure in one of Flaxman's *Odyssey* illustrations (pl. 33). The recumbent
figure, just right of center, may be compared with that of Death, at the
foot of the Cross, in No. XI.

Exhibited: Burlington Fine Arts Club, 1876 [165], lent by Alfred Aspland, who also lent the entire series (excepting No. IIb) to the Grosvenor
Gallery, London, 1877-78, Nos. 353, etc., and the Edinburgh Museum of
Science and Art, 1878, Nos. 146-157; Carfax Gallery, St. James's, London,
1906 (51, A), lent by Sydney Style; The Grolier Club, New York, 1919

(45)—twelve drawings exhibited under this number, lent by Henry E. Huntington; Huntington Library and Art Gallery, 1936—the whole set of thirteen drawings.

Reproduced: Lyceum Press *Paradise Lost*, pl. 2; Nonesuch Press *Poems in English*, I, 10 (Geoffrey Keynes, in his "Notes" on illustrations [I, 356], erroneously states that this illustration is from "the Boston series"; no drawing of this episode is at Boston). The whole set is reproduced in the Catalogue of the Exhibition of Blake's drawings of *Paradise Lost*, Huntington Library and Art Gallery, 1936.

Other Related Versions: (*a*) Victoria and Albert Museum (20 1/4 x 15 3/8 inches; No. 697): this has eight persons in all, and roughly corresponds with the central portion of the Huntington version. Satan is more heavily built and stands on his left foot. The central manacled figure below (in the Huntington drawing) is placed on the right, the head inclined over his right shoulder; immediately below Satan a foreshortened figure on its back, the head forward; another head showing beyond its armpit. The figure in the cave, in the left lower corner, is in both drawings. Reproduced: Wright, *Blake*, II, pl. 63; Collins Baker, *British Painting* (London [1933]), pl. 111. (*b*) Petworth House, Sussex (Lord Leconfield); tempera, 21 x 16 inches: different in design and disposition; Satan stands above the seated angel with back turned; the other figures almost entirely different. Reproduced: Collins Baker, *Catalogue of the Petworth Collection of Pictures* (London, 1920), p. 4. (*c*) Graham Robertson Collection; tempera, 21 1/4 x 16 1/2 inches: this was a "composition for" the Petworth picture; presumably exhibited Burlington Fine Arts Club, 1876 (211), lent by Samuel Palmer.

II^A *Satan Comes to the Gates of Hell* (PLATE II)

SATAN strides from the left, his right leg forward, his spear and shield in his extended hands. On the right the wraith-monster, Death, old and bearded, the progeny of Lucifer and Sin, stays Satan with his flaming dart. In the center, between them, Sin—"the Portress of Hell Gate," a "Woman to the waste, and fair, But ended foul in many a scaly fould," with her hell-hounds and the key of Hell—rises to thrust them apart. In the

[4]

left background red and yellow flames and the cavern of Hell; in the right Hell's latticed gate. *Signed:* "W Blake."

9 3/4 x 8 3/16 inches.

SEE *Paradise Lost*, II, 645, etc.

Exhibited: Burlington Fine Arts club, 1876 [160], lent by Alfred Aspland; Carfax Gallery, St. James's, London, 1906 (51, B), lent by Sydney Style.

Reproduced: Lyceum Press *Paradise Lost*, pl. 3; Nonesuch Press *Poems in English*, I, 48.

II^B *Satan Comes to the Gates of Hell* (PLATE III)

SATAN advances from the left, his left foot forward, his spear poised and shield uplifted. On the right wraith-like Death, beardless, with back turned, prepares to drive his flaming spear into Satan. Center, thrusting them apart, Sin rises above her hellhounds. Two monstrous serpents coil across the flaming ground; flames writhe and flicker in the cavernous background, left and center; on the right Hell's latticed gate. Sin's hair is flamelike; the serpents are iridescent brown, red, and yellow. *Signed:* "inv. W B."

19 1/2 x 15 13/16 inches.

SEE *Paradise Lost*, II, 645, etc. The figure of Sin, with her hellhounds and the coiling snakes, seems to have been based on Flaxman's invention of Scylla (pl. 20 in his illustrations of the *Odyssey*). It is interesting to compare Gillray's caricature, "Sin, Death and the Devil," June 9, 1792, No. 86* in Thomas Wright and R. H. Evans, *Account of the Caricatures of James Gillray* (1851).

Exhibited (perhaps): Burlington Fine Arts Club, 1876 [174], lent by R. P. Cuffe, though the measurement given in the catalogue is 19 1/2 x 13 3/4 inches.

Bibliography: Gilchrist (1880), II, 249 (234), suggesting that this drawing was part of the "Paradise Lost" set formerly in the Butts Collection (now at Boston, lacking this subject).

Another Version: That recorded in Gilchrist (1863), II, 249 (100), and

(1880), II, 268 (128), as belonging (in 1863) to Mr. Harvey, "slightly touched with colour in the Satan ... only half executed."

III *Christ Offers to Redeem Man* (PLATE IV)

THE FATHER sits in light, within the cloud-fringed opening of Heaven, His head bowed on Christ's breast, His hands clasping His Son. Christ, with uplifted arms, His back turned, steps into the Eternal's embrace; two angels on each side swoop down, casting their crowns, "inwove with Amarant and Gold," before His feet. Below, with closed red pinions, Satan floats, "coasting the wall of Heav'n on this side Night in the dun Air sublime." The upper part is white, gray, and faint blue; the lower, rose and brownish-gray. *Signed:* "1807 W.B." [Part of the "7" cut.] 10 1/8 x 8 1/4 inches.

SEE *Paradise Lost*, III, 222, etc. For the Michelangelesque prophetic figure of the Father, cf. Blake's frontispiece to his *Ahania* (1795). The figure of the Redeemer is paralleled in Blake's "Ascension" in the Graham Robertson Collection, *ca.* 1808; in that drawing also there are angels swooping down, but outward. The figure of Satan recurs, virtually the same but in reverse, as Paris, in Blake's "Judgement of Paris" (1817), in the Graham Robertson Collection.

Exhibited: Burlington Fine Arts Club, 1876 [162], lent by Alfred Aspland; Carfax Gallery, St. James's, London, 1906 (51, C), lent by Sydney Style.

Reproduced: Lyceum Press *Paradise Lost*, pl. 10.

Related Version: Museum of Fine Arts, Boston (19 1/5 x 15 3/10 inches). It is more elaborated but practically identical in design, with differences in spacing and in the poses of hands and feet. The Redeemer is older, and His face shown profile left; the Father's right elbow hangs down over His thigh. In the Boston drawing Christ's hands cut across the feet of the swooping angels; Satan grips his spear with all fingers.

What may have been an early idea for the figures of the Father and Son appears on p. 110 of the *Note-Book of William Blake, Called the Rossetti Manuscript* (London: Nonesuch Press, 1935). The Father sits upright, and

Christ stands apart from Him, profile left. Below, a figure reclining (like Michelangelo's "Twilight" figure on the tomb of Lorenzo de Medici) may be an idea for Satan. On p. 104 a sketch shows the Father, with hidden face, embracing the Son, who floats in the air with widespread arms.

IV *Satan's and Raphael's Entries into Paradise* (PLATE V)

TWO scenes combined. On the left Satan, wound round by the Serpent, enters Eden with folded wings, not yet having assumed the guise of a cormorant. On the right Adam and Eve ("erect and tall, Godlike erect, with native Honour clad") walk away, conversing, towards distant woods and mountains. In the center the Angel Raphael, "Seraph wingd," descends in a cloud, looking upward to the Eternal Father, whose wings and arms span the heavens. The sky is grayish-blue, the cloud warm gray; the distant fells and trees are quiet green; Satan's Serpent is gold- and red-scaled. *Signed:* "W Blake 1807."

9 7/8 x 8 inches.

SEE *Paradise Lost*, IV, 172, etc., and V, 277, etc.

Exhibited: Burlington Fine Arts Club, 1876 [119], lent by Alfred Aspland; Carfax Gallery, St. James's, London, 1906 (51, E), lent by Sydney Style.

Reproduced: Lyceum Press *Paradise Lost*, pl. 6; Nonesuch Press *Poems in English*, I, 130.

V *Satan Watches Adam and Eve* (PLATE VI)

ADAM and Eve seated on a bank strewn with nectarine fruits and overarched with flowering palms. Eve, on the left, "half imbracing," leans on Adam, who kisses her, his right hand pressing her face to his. Satan floats above them, wraith-like, with folded wings, communing with his Serpent; at his feet, on the right, the crescent moon and evening star; on the left the sun, above the sea horizon. Glowing light round the sun, dark-gray

sky on right; in the foreground light greens and pale rose pinks.
Signed: "W. Blak[e]." [The "e" cut.]

   10 3/16 x 8 3/8 inches.

S<small>EE</small> *Paradise Lost*, IV, 492, etc.

   Exhibited: Burlington Fine Arts Club, 1876 [114], lent by Alfred Aspland; Carfax Gallery, St. James's, London, 1904 (31), and 1906 (51, D), and Manchester, Whitworth Institute, 1914 (58, 1)—lent by J. Annan Bryce on these three occasions.

   Reproduced: Scott, *Blake: Etchings*, pl. viii; Lyceum Press *Paradise Lost*, pl. 5; Wright, *Blake*, II, pl. 52.

   Other Versions: (*a*) Museum of Fine Arts, Boston (19 1/5 x 15 3/10): more elaborated; in it the flying Satan is reversed, the head being on the right; but one coil of his serpent round the hips. Adam's left arm lies along his side, his left knee touches his right foot, the lower leg extending towards the right corner; Eve's figure slants more to the left. The crescent moon is nearer the horizon, on the left side of the design. (*b*) National Gallery, Melbourne (20 x 15 1/2 inches): ex Linnell Collection and Sale, 1918 (Gilchrist [1863], II, 212 [92]; [1880], II, 223 [112]); exhibited Burlington Fine Arts Club, 1876 (212 or 213). In Gilchrist said to belong to 1822. In design like the Boston version. (*c*) Sydney Morse Sale, 1929, bought by Bunbaum (10 1/2 x 8 inches): signed and dated 1806; ex J. C. Strange and E. B. Tyler collections; probably exhibited Burlington Fine Arts Club, 1876 (121), "Adam and Eve and the Serpent," lent by C. J. Strange. See Gilchrist (1863), II, 209 (71); (1880), II, 217 (83). This drawing is reproduced in Laurence Binyon, *Drawings and Engravings of William Blake* (London, 1922), pl. 70. Satan, turned towards the left, clasps his ears; Eve's right hand is open at shoulder level; Adam's left leg is extended. A vague sketch in the *Note-Book* (p. 100) may be an idea for the figure of Eve, in reverse.

VI *Raphael Warns Adam and Eve* (PLATE VII)

O<small>N THE</small> left Adam and Eve sit together in their bower, hearkening to Raphael's discourse and admonishment. The "winged Hierarch" sits on the right, both arms extended, his "gorgeous wings" joined erect over his head. In the center mid-distance the Serpent, embracing the Tree of Knowledge, and the beasts of the earth [IV, 340, etc.] living in amity. The sky and distance, white and gray; the flowery ground colored with light greens and rose pinks. *Signed:* "W Blake."

10 1/8 x 8 1/4 inches.

SEE *Paradise Lost,* V, 451, etc.

Exhibited: Burlington Fine Arts Club, 1876 [163], lent by Alfred Aspland; Carfax Gallery, St. James's, London, 1904 (32), and 1906 (51, F); and Manchester, Whitworth Institute, 1914 (58, ii)—lent by J. Annan Bryce on these three occasions.

Reproduced: Lyceum Press *Paradise Lost,* pl. 7.

Another Version: A somewhat similar drawing is in the Museum of Fine Arts, Boston (19 1/5 x 15 3/10 inches), but it depicts an earlier stage in this episode. Adam sits alone on the left, his hands raised with palms outwards; Raphael is crowned and his wings are much shorter. Eve stands between them, facing; a cluster of grapes in her right hand, a drinking vessel in her left. The Tree of Knowledge, with surrounding animals, is smaller and more distant.

VII *Rout of the Rebel Angels* (PLATE VIII)

THE MESSIAH kneels within the circular opening of the "Chrystal wall of Heav'n," loosing an arrow into "the wastful Deep." The Rebels fall headlong through flames towards Hell. Three Angels on each side, within the nimbus that surrounds the Son and from which radiate seven arrows. The nimbus is white, the opening into Heaven faint rose; the flames are red, yellow, and blue. *Signed:* "W Blake."

10 3/16 x 8 3/16 inches.

SEE *Paradise Lost,* VI, 835, etc. In the falling rebels reminiscences and adaptations of Michelangelo's "Last Judgment" in the Sistine Chapel can be traced. But it is difficult to reject the idea that Rubens' "Fall of the Damned," at Munich, was also in Blake's mind.

Exhibited: Burlington Fine Arts Club, 1876[115], lent by Alfred Aspland; Carfax Gallery, St. James's, London, 1906 (51, G), lent by Sydney Style.

Reproduced: Lyceum Press *Paradise Lost*, pl. 1.

Another Version: Museum of Fine Arts, Boston (19 1/5 x 15 3/10 inches): elaborated; Christ kneels on both knees; the six angels surrounding Him are more elaborately drawn; the rebel angels are differently posed—e. g., in the Huntington version a profile figure falls on the right; in the Boston version a somewhat similar figure falls on the left. In this version, also, there are no heads under the central falling figure. A drawing in India ink and wash, apparently related to some figures in this design, was exhibited in the Museum of Fine Arts, Boston, 1891 (56), lent by Charles E. West.

A tempera "Fall of the Rebel Angels," on copper, was lot 75 in the Alfred Aspland Sale, January 27, 1885, bought by Gray. Gilchrist ([1880], II, 249 [232]) describes an "oil painting (?) on copper, oval shaped," of this subject; an archangel pursues the falling rebels; "below, the globe of hell opens to receive them"; about forty figures.

VIII *Creation of Eve* (PLATE IX)

ADAM lies asleep on a white cover with foliated edges, his head on the left. The Father stands beyond him on the right, His right hand outstretched above Eve, who floats upward from Adam's side. She looks towards her Creator's face. Pale dawn sky, the crescent moon above; a dim mass of trees hides the horizon. The dawn sky is white, gradating to deep gray; bluish half-tones in the modelling of Adam; the grass is yellow-green. *Signed:* "1807 W B."

10 x 8 3/16 inches.

SEE *Paradise Lost*, VIII, 455, etc.

Exhibited: Burlington Fine Arts Club, 1876 (116), lent by Alfred Aspland; Carfax Gallery, St. James's, London, 1906 (51, H), lent by Sydney Style.

Reproduced: Scott, *Blake: Etchings*, pl. vii; Lyceum Press *Paradise Lost*, pl. 4; Sotheby Catalogue of the Sydney Style Sale, December 15, 1906, facing p. 59; *Burlington Magazine*, X, 293.

Other Versions: (*a*) Museum of Fine Arts, Boston (19 1/5 x 15 3/10 inches): elaborated; the head of the Creator is slightly less bent; Eve looks upward to His raised hand, which is a little to the right of her head; Adam's head and neck, surrounded by the cover, are lower on the bank; his left hand is seen; his knees and feet touch. The foliage and trunks of the grove are outlined in detail; the sky is darker and the crescent more upright. (*b*) National Gallery, Melbourne (20 x 16 inches): ex Linnell Collection and Sale, 1918 (Gilchrist [1863], II, 212 [91]; [1880], II, 223 [111]).* Exhibited Manchester, Whitworth Institute, 1914 (2). Virtually a replica of the Boston version; Christ's drapery divided into many more folds; but less linear detail in the background trunks and foliage. (*c*) Gilchrist ([1863], II, 223 [106]; [1880] II, 235 [129]) records "The Creation of Eve" in the Milnes† Collection ("The Creator holding a hand of Adam, who reclines under a vine, and a hand of Eve, upon a floating cloud").‡

IX *Temptation and Fall of Eve* (PLATE X)

EVE stands center, under the fruit-laden Tree of Knowledge. The Serpent, twined about her, puts a fruit to her lips. Adam, unaware, stands with back turned, in the left background. The sky and distant hills are in gray wash; notes of green and red in the foliage, the fruit, and the Serpent. Lightning, nature's "signs of woe," rends the sky. *Signed:* "1807 W B."

10 x 8 1/4 inches.

SEE *Paradise Lost*, IX, 630, etc.

Exhibited: Burlington Fine Arts Club, 1876 [117], lent by Alfred Aspland; Carfax Gallery, St. James's, London, 1906 (51, I), lent by Sydney Style.

Reproduced: Scott, *Blake: Etchings*, pl. ix; Lyceum Press *Paradise Lost*, pl. 8; Wright, *Blake*, II, pl. 53.

Other Versions: Museum of Fine Arts, Boston (19 1/5 x 5 3/10 inches): elaborated; Eve stands more upright; the coils of the serpent surrounding her are simpler and fewer; the tree is covered with a thorny growth; the landscape has a lower horizon, and some of the hills are replaced by groves; the lightning on the right is more perpendicular. An "Eve Tempted by the Serpent" was lent by Captain Stirling to the Glasgow Exhibition, 1902

* In Gilchrist said to belong to 1822. † Later Lord Houghton and Earl of Crewe.
‡ In the 1880 edition no owner is given.

(118), to the Tate Gallery Exhibition, 1913 (3), and to the Manchester Whitworth Institute, 1914 (4). It is in tempera (10 x 14 3/4 inches) and shows Adam lying asleep and Eve standing full face, her right arm raised (Gilchrist [1863], II, 223 [107], and [1880], II, 235 [130]). In the 1863 edition, Stirling's name is attached to No. 107. An "Adam, Eve and Serpent" was lot 100 in the Butts Sale, June 29, 1853, bought by Bohn; a drawing with the same title (10 1/2 x 7 3/4 inches) was exhibited at the Burlington Fine Arts Club, 1876 (121), lent by C. J. Strange. These probably illustrated "Satan Watching Adam and Eve" (see No. V).

X *Judgment of Adam and Eve* (PLATE XI)

THE SON, "mild Judge and Intercessor," stands between Adam and Eve, His hands raised, pronouncing judgment. On the right Eve hides her bowed face; on the left Adam listens with hands joined. At their feet the "accurst" Serpent prone on the ground; above, on the left, Death looses his black-tipped shafts, and on the right Sin with her hellhounds pours flames from two vials. Dark-gray sky with gray-blue horizon; massed dull-green trees; light-green ground; Sin's hounds have red and yellow scales. *Signed:* "W Blake."

9 7/8 x 8 inches.

SEE *Paradise Lost*, X, 103, etc.

Exhibited: Burlington Fine Arts Club, 1876 [164], lent by Alfred Aspland; Carfax Gallery, St. James's, London, 1906 (51, J), lent by Sydney Style.

Reproduced: Lyceum Press *Paradise Lost*, pl. 9; Nonesuch Press *Poems in English*, I, 268 (Keynes, in his "Notes" [p. 358], erroneously states that this illustration is "from the Boston series"; no drawing of this episode is at Boston).

XI *Michael Foretells the Crucifixion* (PLATE XII)

CHRIST hangs on the Cross against a dark sky; on the left stands Michael pointing to the vision; on the right Adam, looking upward with joined hands. Across the foreground Eve lies asleep in a flower-fringed *mandorla*. The nail through Christ's feet transfixes the dead, ashen Serpent; the Cross is planted between dead Sin and Death. The sky is white, gradating to black; notes of red, green, and yellow. *Signed:* "1807 W B."

10 x 8 inches.

SEE *Paradise Lost*, XII, 411, etc.

Exhibited: Burlington Fine Arts Club, 1876 [161], lent by Alfred Aspland; Carfax Gallery, St. James's, London, 1906 (51, K), lent by Sydney Style.

Reproduced: Scott, *Blake: Etchings*, pl. x (lithograph); Lyceum Press *Paradise Lost*, pl. 11.

Other Versions: (*a*) Museum of Fine Arts, Boston (19 1/5 x 14 9/10 inches): elaborated; Michael stands nearer to the Cross; his left arm is more bent; his right hand is dropped beside him; his helmet is more heavily plumed and fills the space between the wing tops; his left wing comes in front of the left arm of Death. The Serpent's head is plumed and two coils close together surround the Cross; the inscription, "INRI," is not shown. (*b*) Mrs. J. H. Riches' Collection (19 3/4 or 20 x 15 1/4 inches): ex Linnell Collection and Sale, 1918 (Gilchrist [1863], II, 212 [93]; II, 223 [113]). Exhibited Burlington Fine Arts Club, 1876 (212 or 213),* and Burlington Fine Arts Club, 1927 (48).

XII *The Expulsion* (PLATE XIII)

THE ARCHANGEL Michael, with closed wings and plumed casque, advances in the center, leading Adam with his right hand and Eve with his left; he treads over the Serpent. Adam, his right arm raised, looks up, as does Eve, at a vast coiling flame, the "flaming Brand," "fierce as a Comet," that will shut them from Paradise. Above, four mounted cherubim stand against flames and golden light, guarding the entrance ("the Gate with dreadful Faces throng'd and fierie Armes"). Thorns and thistles strew the ground; lightning rends the sky. Faint notes of gold and rose color. *Signed:* "1807 W B."

* In Gilchrist said to belong to 1822.

9 7/8 x 8 1/16 inches.

SEE *Paradise Lost*, XII, 637-40.

Exhibited: Burlington Fine Arts Club, 1876 [118], lent by Alfred Aspland; Carfax Gallery, St. James's, London, 1906 (51, L), lent by Sydney Style.

Reproduced: Lyceum Press *Paradise Lost*, pl. 12.

Another Version: Museum of Fine Arts, Boston (19 1/5 x 14 9/10 inches): elaborated; St. Michael is full-face, looking to the left front; his helmet is more plumed; his left hand grips the wrist of Eve; she and Adam look down at the Serpent. The heads of the four Riders and their horses are dark. The flame above is less massive and cuts in front of Michael's left wing.

Bibliography:

William Bell Scott, *William Blake: Etchings from His Works* (London, 1878), pp. 7-8 and plates.

Gilchrist (1880), II, 218 (85).

Richard Garnett, *William Blake, Painter and Poet* (London, 1895), p. 62.

Paradise Lost, by John Milton; Illustrations by William Blake (Liverpool: Lyceum Press [Liverpool Booksellers Co.], 1906). [The Huntington Library set reproduced in color.]

Keynes, *Bibliography*, p. 301 (229).

John Milton, Poems in English, with Illustrations by William Blake (London: Nonesuch Press, 1926), I, 355-59 ("Notes" by Geoffrey Keynes on illustrations).

Mona Wilson, *Life of William Blake* (London: Nonesuch Press, 1927), pp. 201, 332, 359.

Thomas Wright, *Life of William Blake* (Olney, 1929), II, 167-68.

Collections: Of the Huntington Library set of thirteen drawings, illustrating *Paradise Lost*, all but IIb were owned by Alfred Aspland, of Dukinfield and Liverpool. These twelve were in his sale at Sotheby's, January 27, 1885, lots 77-88; ten of them (Nos. I, IIa, III, IV, VII-XII) were bought by Pincott and acquired by Sydney Style, of Liverpool; in his sale, Sotheby's, December 15, 1906 (481), bought by Sabin; Nos. V and VI were bought by Gray (lots 80 and 83), and acquired by J. Annan Bryce, and, apparently, sold privately by him in 1914. No. IIb may have been in the R. P. Cuffe Collection, *ca.* 1876; in the H. A. J. Munro sale, April 22, 1868, and a Different Properties Sale, Christie's, July 19, 1907 (4b), bought by Sabin; in his possession till 1911; passed to an American buyer. Mr.

Huntington acquired the Style group in 1911; the two from the Bryce collection in 1914; and IIb in 1916.

The Boston *Paradise Lost* series (nine drawings) is recorded in Gilchrist (1863), II, 209-10 (75), under the year 1808; (1880), II, 219 (90). It was exhibited at the Burlington Fine Arts Club, 1876 [158, 159, 175-81], lent by C. J. Strange; Museum of Fine Arts, Boston, 1891 (25, a-i), the property of the Museum. This series is reproduced in Darrell Figgis, *Paintings of William Blake* (London, 1925), plates 14-22, and in part in the Nonesuch Press *Poems in English*, pp. 74, 104, 114, 136, 180, 218, 250, 352. One of the Boston series—"Adam & Eve Sleeping"—is not repeated in the Huntington Library set.

Six Illustrations to Milton's "On the Morning of Christ's Nativity" (*ca*. 1808)

I *The Descent of Peace* (PLATE XIV)

THE SPIRIT of Peace descends, her arms inclosing the gable of the hut, wherein the Virgin, robed in white, kneels leaning back against the supporting arms of St. Joseph, in a blue coat. Opposite kneel Zacharias and St. Elizabeth, the little St. John on her knees. In the center the newborn Infant rises in a glory of Light. At the back, the heads of an aged man and two oxen. On the snow before the hut lies the snow-veiled figure of Nature (verses I-II). In the background, rime-covered plants and snowy clouds, beneath the arc of a wintry sun circled with pink. *Signed:* "W. Blake."

6 5/16 x 5 inches.

SEE verses I-III. In pose and grouping, the Virgin and St. Joseph correspond with the mother and father of Moses in Blake's "Hiding of Moses" in this collection, and (in reverse) with the Virgin and St. Joseph in Blake's tempera "Nativity," No. 13 in the Burlington Fine Arts Exhibition, 1927, lent by Sydney Morse, and now in America. See the catalogue of that exhibition for a suggestion that Blake may have used the design in a Roman bas-relief of the "Birth of Dionysus," for his little figure of the Babe, springing forth in light. Somewhat similar motifs are seen in his "Compassion of Pharaoh's Daughter" and his tempera "Flight into Egypt," both in the Graham Robertson collection, the latter dated 1790.

Exhibited: The Grolier Club, New York, 1919 (42); the six drawings exhibited under this number, lent by Henry E. Huntington.

Another Version: Manchester, Whitworth Institute. The Virgin kneels upright, cradling the Babe in her arms; St. Joseph bends over her, profile left. On the left two oxen feed from the manger. The Spirit of Peace is reversed, her head on the left of the gable. Nature also is reversed, her head left; both legs are seen, but snow encircles the hips. The drawing of rime and snowcloud is more mannered and defined. *Signed:* "W. Blake 1809." 9 1/2 x 7 1/2 inches.

II *Shepherds and the Heavenly Choir* (PLATE XIV)

THE SHEPHERDS, in coats of dull blue, rose, and neutral green, sit across the front of the picture, looking up to the naked hymning Cherubim and Seraphim, in "a globe of circular light." A ram lies in the right, a dog in the left, foreground. Beyond, another dog with flocks and tents; in the distance the hut of the Nativity. *Signed:* "W. Blake."
6 1/4 x 5 7/8 inches.

SEE verses VIII-XI.

Another Version: Manchester, Whitworth Institute. The shepherd seated in the center foreground looks up to the left. Two bearded shepherds on the right, profile left; one wears a hood. Two younger people of feminine aspect kneel on left, profile right; beyond them a boy, full-face, his left hand on the head of a dog. The hymning angels in the circle of glory are robed and winged; two of them are bearded. Eight angels encircle the standing figures; some have harps, and one has a lute. Below them the hut of the Nativity, showing the Virgin and St. Joseph. *Signed:* "W. Blake 1809." 10 x 7 1/2 inches.

III *"The Old Dragon Underground . . . Swindges the Scaly Horrour of His Foulded Tail"* (PLATE XV)

THE old Dragon sits in the center, seven-headed, horned, and sceptered; his flesh mottled gray and red, his tail slaty. The figures on either side of him are ghostly white. Below, kneels a scaled, web-footed figure. The Dragon's scaly tail breaks through the earth into a whirl of star-filled light. In the distance the hut of the Nativity, three kneeling figures before it. *Signed:* "W. Blake."
6 1/4 x 4 7/8 inches.

SEE verse XVIII. Geoffrey Keynes, in his arrangement of the illustrations (*On the Morning of Christ's Nativity; Milton's Hymn*), attaches the Manchester,Whitworth Institute, version of this drawing to verses XXV-XXVI, "Typhon, huge ending in snaky twine" and the gods trooping "to th' infernall jail."

Another Version: Manchester, Whitworth Institute. The Dragon has six heads, three of them bearded; his right hand holds a three-lobed scepter, his left points upward; his ankles are crossed. The scaly tail is more coiled; one fold surrounds the Dragon. The coils writhe up to right into the band of star-filled light; there is no scaly, web-footed creature in front. The hut is larger and shows the Virgin and Babe with one kneeling figure. The division of the Earth's crust from the cavernous dark is more defined. The figures surrounding the Dragon are more numerous. *Signed:* "W. Blake 18 .." 9 1/2 x 7 1/2 inches.

IV *The Overthrow of Apollo and the Pagan Gods*
(PLATE XV)

APOLLO stands center, the base of his pedestal lapped by red flame. Behind, left, the "parting Genius," in a cloud of lemon-yellow fire, dives towards the waters. Below him, in the distance, a small figure, presumably a haunting spirit of the spring. The four figures prostrated below Apollo may be the "Tyrian maids." The half-naked woman in a cavern on the right may be one of "the Nimphs," mourning in "Twilight shade of tangled thickets."* The clouded night sky is set with vague, spectral shapes, flying from a ruined portico, presumably "the steep of Delphos." *Signed:* "W. Blake."

6 1/4 x 4 7/8 inches.

SEE verses XIX-XXII. The Apollo is derived from the "Pythian" Apollo.

Another Version: Manchester, Whitworth Institute. Apollo, without his cloak, holds in both hands a serpent. At the foot of the Shrine, two women on right, kneeling, and one on left; beyond her, two bearded priests. Be-

---

* In the more highly wrought version at Manchester the cavern is composed of tree trunks and interlacing branches, schematized.

tween Apollo and the descending Genius is the star of the Nativity. Winged forms with animal heads fly overhead. On the right a figure soars above a group surrounding an altar (?). This may be the intention in the vague, blurred figures in the Huntington version. In the Manchester drawing the more defined classical portico extends behind Apollo. *Signed:* "W. Blake." 9 1/2 x 7 1/2 inches.

V *The Flight of Moloch* (PLATE XVI)

"SULLEN Moloch," with red bat-wings, matching his flesh, flies up to right. His wings resemble those of Satan in the "Smiting of Job." Sitting center, with crown and scepter, and surrounded by flame, is his "Idol all of blackest hue" (verse XXIII). A baby hangs from his left hand, two others reach up in supplication, on left. Dancers with cymbals on either side. Below the Idol stands the Babe ("our Babe . . . can in his swaddling bands confront the damned crew"). Two figures kneel in the foreground, turning away in dismay. *Signed:* "W. Blake."

6 1/4 x 4 7/8 inches.

Another Version: Manchester, Whitworth Institute. The bearded idol fills the center, holding a three-lobed scepter against his left shoulder. A baby hangs from his right hand; two others are near his left foot. Below him, the woman kneels on the right, the man on the left; the Babe stands in reverse. The cymbal players on the right advance (the foremost is bearded); those on the left recede. The face of the winged figure overhead does not show. The smoke forms a definite pattern on either side of his wings; ragged mountain peaks along the horizon. *Signed:* "W. Blake 1809." 9 1/2 x 7 1/2 inches.

VI *"The Virgin Blest Hath Laid Her Babe to Rest"* (PLATE XVI)

IN THE center, seen through a foliated doorway, the Virgin kneels asleep, sunk back against the manger in which the Babe sleeps, surrounded by light. St. Joseph, in a blue robe, watches over them, half-asleep. Two angels above the shed, harping; two, with wings folded back along the slopes of the roof; two, "bright-harnest," sit on either side of the entrance. The color of all is shadowy rose. Above, "Heaven's youngest teemed Star," with chariot and "Handmaid lamp attending." *Signed:* "W. Blake." 6 1/4 x 4 7/8 inches.

SEE verse XXVII.

Another Version: Manchester, Whitworth Institute. The Virgin leans back, asleep; her right arm on the manger, the hand supporting her face. St. Joseph, resting on his crossed arms, watches the Babe, lying across the manger. The angels on the roof are bearded; those at the entrance sit up-right, facing, heads erect. The "teemed Star" and her steeds turn their heads to right; one wheel of the chariot shows. *Signed:* "W. Blake 1809." 9 1/2 x 7 1/2 inches.

Reproduced: The Huntington Library six drawings were reproduced in the Nonesuch Press *Poems in English*, II, 4-12.

Bibliography:

Gilchrist (1863), II, 234 (307), "Mrs. de Putron from Mr. Butts"; not entered in the 1880 edition under this name; instead (p. 222 [105]), six illustrations, dated 1809, of Milton's hymn on the Nativity are given, with no owner (presumably the Manchester set, which is so dated).

On the Morning of Christ's Nativity; Milton's Hymn, with Illustrations by William Blake and a Note by Geoffrey Keynes (Cambridge, 1923), p. 32.

Nonesuch Press *Poems in English*, pp. 272-74 ("Notes" by Geoffrey Keynes on illustrations).

Wilson, *Blake*, p. 203.

Wright, *Blake*, II, 169.

Collections: Said to have been* in the collection of B. G. Windus, of Tottenham Green, who died *ca.* 1868; later associated with the name of Mrs. de Putron, of Rodwell Rectory, Dorsetshire. This set of the Nativity drawings appeared in the sale at Christie's, March 16, 1912 (lot 6, bought by Sabin), as "the property of a gentleman, and formerly in the collection

---

* The Huntington Library set is inscribed in Mr. Sabin's writing (vouched for by A. Edward Newton, who organized the Grolier Club Exhibition of Blake's works) : "These drawings were made by Blake for Mr. Butts and passed from him to Mrs. de Putron of Rodwell Rectory."

of B. G. Windus." When part of the B. G. Windus library was sold in 1923, it was stated that the "late Rev. G. P. de Putron," of Guernsey, was his grandson.* Gilchrist mentions in his 1880 edition, II, 222 (105), "1809. Six illustrations to Milton's Hymn for the Nativity," giving no owner; Keynes repeats the gist of his account in his "Notes" in the Nonesuch Press *Poems in English*, II, 272. He adds: "The colouring of the Manchester set is subdued in tint, but light in effect and the drawing is more precise. The effect of the Huntington set is considerably darker and the lines of the drawing have been subordinated to the brush work." Mr. Keynes had not been able to see the Huntington set at the time he made this note. The photographs, by which he judged, somewhat misled him as to the Huntington drawings being "considerably darker." Most of them, with their pale, luminous color, are far brighter than the Manchester relatively monochrome set. As regards the provenance of the two series, it seems that the J. E. Taylor set (now at Manchester) is not identical with Mrs. de Putron's (now at the Huntington Library). Only one set appeared in the Butts sales (March 26, 1852, at Sotheby's, and June 29, 1853, at Foster's; as lot 147 in the former); it was bought by H. Bohn, of York Street, who also bought "And the Angel . . . lifted up his hand," which Gilchrist ([1863], II, 229 [172]) lists as Mrs. de Putron's.

Acquired: In New York, 1916.

The Manchester set is in brown monochrome, with tinted passages; is far more elaborated and linear in conception and treatment. It is reproduced in *On the Morning of Christ's Nativity*, and mentioned in the Nonesuch Press *Poems in English*, II (p. 272). It was exhibited, wholly or in part, at the Burlington Fine Arts Club, 1876 (86 and 102-106), lent by J. E. Taylor; Glasgow, 1902; Tate Gallery, London, 1913 (49 i and ii) [the catalogue giving Mrs. de Putron as a former owner], lent by the Whitworth Institute; Manchester, Whitworth Institute, 1914 (63, i-vi) [similar mention of Mrs. de Putron]; National Gallery of Scotland, Edinburgh, 1914 (74-76); Burlington Fine Arts Club, 1927 (47) [similar mention of Mrs. de Putron]. The entry in Gilchrist (1880), II, 222 (105), "1809.—Six Illustrations to Milton's 'Hymn for the Nativity,'" presumably refers to this Manchester set.

* Keynes (in his "Note" on the illustrations to *On the Morning of Christ's Nativity* [p. 31]) gives Blake's Manchester set of "Nativity" drawings the following pedigree:
  Probably bought, shortly after production, by Thomas Butts: Butts' Sale, March 26, 1852 (147); later in the possession of Mrs. de Putron and also of J. E. Taylor (*temp.* Burlington Fine Arts Club Exhibition, 1876); subsequently presented by J. E. Taylor to the Whitworth Institute, Manchester. Keynes refers to "a second set of drawings," unrecorded and with unknown history, until its appearance at Christie's auction on March 16, 1912.

Eight Illustrations to Milton's "Comus"
(*ca*. 1801)

I *Comus with His Revellers* (PLATE XVII)

THE LADY sits on the right, on a rock. Above and behind her, Comus rushing to the left; with him, the monsters bearing candles. In the top left, the attendant Spirit descending. A grove of trees across the background. The color is moonlight blue; the figures are pallid. *Signed:* "W. B. inv."

8 9/16 x 7 1/8 inches.

SEE *Comus*, ll. 64-82 and stage direction.

Exhibited: The eight drawings, Burlington Fine Arts Club, 1876 (10, 12-17, 22), lent by Alfred Aspland; Tate Gallery, London, 1913 (50, i-viii), lent by Mr. Sabin; Manchester, Whitworth Institute, 1914 (62, i-viii), lent by Mr. Sabin; Grolier Club, New York, 1919 (44)—the eight drawings exhibited under this number.

Another Version: Museum of Fine Arts, Boston, entitled "Comus Holds the Enchanting Cup." The Lady's face and torso are turned right; Comus, close to the right side of the picture, above the Lady's head, is nearly full front, a goblet in his left hand; little of the tree trunks is seen; four monsters appear but no attendant Spirit. *Signed:* "W. Blake." 5 9/10 x 4 3/4 inches. Exhibited Burlington Fine Arts Club, 1876 (137, ii), lent by C. J. Strange.

II *Comus, Disguised as a Rustic, Addresses the Lady in the Wood* (PLATE XVII)

THE LADY stands full front, in moonlight, looking to the left towards Comus disguised as an old rustic in a long, gray cloak, a hat in his right hand. On the right rises the crowned attendant Spirit, with drapery and wings of moonlit blue, a golden blossom in his right hand. He wears a crown of light, and rays of light emanate from him. The background grove is shadowy-green and brownish-gray. *Signed:* "W. B. inv."

8 9/16 x 7 1/8 inches.

SEE *Comus*, ll. 83-85, 145-50, 244-69.

Another Version: Museum of Fine Arts, Boston. There are four instead of two foreground tree trunks. The Spirit's feet almost touch the ground, and his wings point upwards. His robe is transparent; Comus is as a younger rustic. *Signed:* "W. Blake." 5 9/10 x 4 3/4 inches. Exhibited Burlington Fine Arts Club, 1876 (137, i), lent by C. J. Strange.

III *The Brothers Plucking Grapes* (PLATE XVIII)

COMUS, disguised as a rustic, in a pale robe, stands in the left foreground, facing three-quarters left, his head bending right; the eyes look up at the brothers who, dressed in pale blue, are climbing among the branches of a vine. Behind them, a rock; beyond it, the heads of a peasant and his ox. The attendant Spirit shows in the distance, surrounded by rays of pale light in a blue sky. The swords of the brothers lie at the foot of the vine. A small figure sits beneath the distant grove. *Signed:* "W. B."

8 9/10 x 7 1/8 inches.

SEE *Comus*, ll. 290-303.

Another Version: Museum of Fine Arts, Boston. In this version, the head of Comus is more raised; the vine grows on a bank which one brother climbs, reaching up his hand to receive a cluster of grapes from the hand of the other. There are no swords and the attendant Spirit is high in the heavens, in a nimbus of light. *Signed:* "W. Blake." 5 9/10 x 4 3/4 inches. Exhibited Burlington Fine Arts Club, 1876 (137, iv), lent by C. J. Strange.

IV *The Two Brothers Passing the Night in the Wood*
(PLATE XVIII)

THE brothers stand right and left, leaning on bare swords and facing the central figure of the attendant Spirit, disguised as a young shepherd. He holds a crook within his bent left arm and a golden flower in his right hand. His clothes are tinged with yellow; those of the brothers with blue. Two tree trunks with interlacing branches overarch the group. Above them a bending figure driving a chariot, drawn by dragons with fiery scales. *Signed:* "W. B."

8 7/8 x 7 1/16 inches.

SEE *Comus*, ll. 489 ff.

Another Version: Museum of Fine Arts, Boston, entitled "The Attendant Spirit with the Two Brothers." Four tree trunks form three arches, each framing a figure. The brother on the left stands full front, his left hand raised, palm outwards. The Shepherd's left arm is beside him, his fingers holding the crook. The second brother stands with back turned, his head profile left. A crescent moon shows above the chariot. *Signed:* "W. Blake." 5 9/10 x 4 3/4 inches. Exhibited Burlington Fine Arts Club, 1876 (137, iii), lent by C. J. Strange.

V *Comus, with the Lady Spellbound in the Chair*
(PLATE XIX)

THE LADY, in a white robe, sits left, on a square, carved chair, facing three-quarters right, her hands crossed before her waist. Comus, in a dull-pink cloak, stands on the right facing, his right hand holding the magic wand above the Lady's head, his left clasping the goblet (line 810). Two figures with owllike heads and horned wings stand in the left background. Three others, beaked, sit behind the table, on which are drinking vessels. The background of arches is greenish-yellow, lit by hanging lamps. The tables and vessels are grayish, with pink and blue iridescence. *Signed:* "W. B."

8 3/4 x 7 1/16 inches.

SEE *Comus*, ll. 658-64 and stage direction, ll. 810-12.

Another Version: Museum of Fine Arts, Boston, entitled "The Magic Banquet." Comus stands with his feet closer together, his left hand more raised. The owllike figures are omitted, and two of the beaked figures replaced by an elephant and a lion. A ghoulish figure with a salver and chalice stands behind the Lady's chair, left, and another, with a cat's head, bearing a flagon, behind her, right. *Signed:* "W. Blake." 5 9/10 x 4 3/4 inches. Exhibited Burlington Fine Arts Club, 1876 (138, v), lent by C. J. Strange.

VI *The Brothers Driving Out Comus* (PLATE XIX)

COMUS flees to the left, looking back at the brothers, who rush upon him with raised swords, the nearer having seized the goblet in his left hand. The Lady, in a white robe touched with pink, sits on the right, gazing upwards. Behind her a coiling cloud of smoky vapor, rose, blue, and white, in which a swinging lamp shows. Behind Comus' staff the heads of fiends and monsters. *Signed:* "W. B. inv."

8 3/4 x 7 inches.

SEE *Comus*, l. 813 and stage direction.

Another Version: Museum of Fine Arts, Boston, entitled "The Brothers Overcome Comus." Comus, on the left, is facing; the Lady sits center, facing right, her hands on her knees. In right background a grove of trees. *Signed:* "W. Blake." 5 9/10 x 4 3/4 inches. Exhibited Burlington Fine Arts Club, 1876 (138, vi), lent by C. J. Strange.

VII *Sabrina Disenchanting the Lady* (PLATE XX)

THE LADY, robed in white faintly tinged with pink, sits center, on a bank, by the root of a tree. Sabrina and four attendant Spirits on the right, drifting with feet clear of the ground. Sabrina sprinkles holy water on the Lady's face. All are clothed in whitish, iridescent robes. On the left the brothers, bending over their sister, and behind them, the attendant Spirit, disguised as a shepherd, pointing skyward. Above are heavy, spreading tree trunks, through which a dark-green hill-top shows against a starlit sky. A greenish tint pervades. *Signed:* "W. B. inv."

8 1/2 x 7 1/8 inches.

SEE *Comus*, ll. 907-20.

Another Version: Museum of Fine Arts, Boston. The Lady's hands are extended; Sabrina, with only two attendant Spirits, is much lower in the picture and almost kneeling, her right hand on a level with the Lady's shoulder. The nearer brother's right arm hangs down; an arc of light is over Sabrina, and the background is of undulating wooded hills, without tree trunks. *Signed:* "W. Blake." 5 9/10 x 4 3/4 inches. Exhibited Burlington Fine Arts Club, 1876 (138, vii), lent by C. J. Strange.

VIII *The Lady Restored to Her Parents* (PLATE XX)

THE LADY stands three-quarters right, her left hand clasped by her father's, her waist encircled by her mother's right arm. The brothers stand facing, looking up, left, to the figure of the attendant Spirit, who rises with spread wings. On the right an open doorway under flat eaves. Behind a hill, the sun rises, throwing strong shadows on the bright-green foreground. *Signed:* "W. B."

8 7/8 x 7 inches.

SEE *Comus*, l. 945 and stage direction.

Another Version: Museum of Fine Arts, Boston, entitled "The Parents Welcome the Children." The Lady stands profile right, her parents, on the right, bending towards her. The nearer brother and departing attendant Spirit have their backs turned, the latter with his arms stretched, as in blessing, towards the rising sun. The structure on the right has a slanting roof, and a grove of trees fills the background. *Signed:* "W. Blake." 5 9/10 x 4 3/4 inches. Exhibited Burlington Fine Arts Club, 1876 (138, viii), lent by C. J. Strange.

Reproduced: Nonesuch Press *Poems in English*, II, 58-85 (according to Keynes, in his "Notes" [p. 277], some of the drawings were reproduced in autotype by the English Picture Publishing Company in 1874). No. VI is reproduced in Wright's *Blake*, II, pl. 49.

Bibliography:

Gilchrist (1880), II, 246 (a brief mention in connection with the Butts [now Boston] set).

Archibald G. B. Russell, *Letters of William Blake* (London [1906]), p. 95 (October 19, 1801: "I have promised him [Mr. Thomas] to send my designs for *Comus* when I have done them.").

Wilson, *Blake*, pp. 132, 352.

Wright, *Blake*, I, 10, 114; II, 167.

Nonesuch Press *Poems in English*, II. Keynes, in his "Notes" (p. 277), comments: "The drawings are considerably larger than the others [i.e., the Boston set] . . . and they are, on the whole, much more beautiful."

Collections: In Alfred Aspland's, in 1876; in his sale, Sotheby's, January 27, 1885, lots 94-101, seven of the series were bought by Colnaghi, and the eighth ("Comus with the Lady Spellbound," lot 98) were bought by Riggall. In 1913 the eight drawings were in Mr. Frank Sabin's possession.

Acquired: In New York, 1916.

The Boston series was bought by C. J. Strange from Thomas Butts's sale, at Foster's, Pall Mall, June 29, 1853 (98). It is recorded in Gilchrist (1863), II, 232 (205, a-h), and (1880), II, 245-46 (230, a-h); it was reproduced in colored lithographs by William Griggs, in Bernard Quaritch, *Facsimiles of Choice Examples Selected from Illuminated Manuscripts, Unpublished Drawings* . . . (London, 1890), Pt. II. Nos. 3, 6, and 8 are illustrated in Figgis, *Paintings*, plates 97-99; the whole series is reproduced in John Milton, *Comus: A Mask* (London, 1926; "Julian Editions"), with preface by Darrell Figgis.

It was exhibited, Burlington Fine Arts Club, 1876 (137-38), lent by C. J. Strange; Museum of Fine Arts, Boston, 1891 (26, a-h).

Other Water-Color Drawings

The Hiding of Moses (PLATE XXI)

JOCHEBED, the mother of Moses, kneels in the right corner, on the left bank, leaning back against her husband Amram's knee; a white robe covers her from the waist down. The man wears a bluish robe, his chest, left shoulder, and arm bare. A thick palm tree leans over them. Center, the infant Moses (only pencilled) lies afloat in his cradle. From the palm tree, on the right, to left of center a stepped wall extends; on the lowest step a sphinx crouches; on the third, her back turned, stands Amram's sister, "afar off to wit what would be done to him"; she wears a yellow skirt. The Nile meanders from the left foreground towards the center distance. In the left distance two pyramids loom against the sky; a variety of buildings and structures, some spired, some monolithic, in the center distance and left mid-distance.

11 1/4 x 15 3/4 inches.

IN POSE and grouping, the mother and father correspond with the SS. Joseph and Mary in "The Descent of Peace," p. 16.

Engraved by Blake as an illustration in *Remember Me! A New Year's Gift or Christmas Present* (London, 1825), p. 32.

Reproduced: Keynes, *Bibliography*, p. 215; Binyon, *Engraved Designs*, pl. 15.

Bibliography:

Gilchrist ([1863], II, 224 [114]; [1880], II, 235 [137]) describes a tempera painting in the Butts Collection, apparently corresponding with this water color; Binyon (*Engraved Designs*, No. 104) opines that the tempera picture is lost, and that the water color was made for the engraving.

* Keynes assumes the date to be *ca.* 1825, from the engraving that Blake made in 1825 from the drawing. But the drawing may have been made several years before.

Archibald G. B. Russell, *Engravings of William Blake* (1912), p. 102 (32).
Keynes, *Bibliography*, p. 215 (78).
Laurence Binyon, *Engraved Designs of William Blake* (London, 1926),
No. 104, pl. 15.
Wright, *Blake*, II, 171.
Collections: Perhaps Thomas Butts; in his sale, June 29, 1853 (Foster's),
two pictures of "Moses and Pharaoh's Daughter" (lots 84 and 126) were
sold; possibly one was the "Hiding of Moses." John Linnell; his sale,
March 15, 1918 (156), bought by Robson.

Conversion of Saul, ca. 1798 (PLATE XXII)

SAUL is mounted on a dapple-gray horse, fallen to the ground,
profile left. His hair and beard are light red. The cloak over
his right shoulder is yellow. He looks up, "trembling and as-
tonished," to the Lord, who floats in a golden light from Heaven,
His right arm directing Saul to Damascus. He is surrounded by
seraphim, and from Him bars of shadow and half-light radiate
athwart the stormy sky. Beyond Saul are seen the bowed and
huddled forms of his companions, in casques and armor, one
face, only, free. *Signed:* "W. B. inv. " The margin is inscribed,
"Acts ix c 6v."

The sheet of paper, 16 5/8 x 14 5/8 inches; the drawing, con-
fined by an ink line, 16 1/8 x 14 1/8 inches.

THIS drawing must be approximately contemporary with "Death on the
Pale Horse," in the Fitzwilliam Museum. Figgis suggested *ca.* 1805 for the
latter; but this appears to be some years too late.

Bibliography:

Gilchrist (1863), II, 229 (167), ex Butts; (1880), II, 242 (191), ex Butts.
Wright, *Blake*, II, 173.
Collections: Presumably in Thomas Butts's; his sale, March 26, 1852
(Sotheby's), lot 152, bought by Colnaghi.
This drawing was found in the extra-illustrated copy of John Kitto's

edition of the Bible, among the prints and drawings mainly collected by James Gibbs, the London dealer, before 1836. His son John (?) Gibbs, and possibly Theodore Irwin, Sr., a book collector of Oswego, New York, added items. This Bible is in the Theodore Irwin Catalogue of 1887 (No. 180); the catalogue states that James Gibbs's collection of material "has since undergone an extensive change."

Acquired: In 1919 (with the Bible volumes), from Theodore Irwin, Jr.

HAND-COLORED PRINT

Lucifer and the Pope in Hell

THE POPE, in tiara and long, red gown, his hands hidden in its folds, stands to the right front, his face profile right. Lucifer appears beyond him, scaly and with wind-blown hair, stretching his right arm and spear horizontally across the sky. The left leg and black cloak seen behind the Pope. In the left background a mound of human heads before a mass of flames: three of them are crowned and bearded; three others partly seen. The sky is dark Prussian blue gradating almost to black; the flames are rust-colored.

7 11/16 x 10 5/8 inches.

Exhibited: Burlington Fine Arts Club, 1876 (167), lent by George Smith.

Other Versions: In the Museum of Fine Arts, Boston, is a water-color drawing of this subject, reproduced in Darrell Figgis' *Blake* (pl. 85) and called "The King of Babylon in Hell." It is a different design; Lucifer stands center, holding the Pope's manacles; a monstrosity falls from the sky on the extreme right. This print is identical with, or a replica of, that recorded in Gilchrist (1880), II, 216 (71), dated 1805. Two similar undated designs are recorded in Gilchrist (1880), II, 253 (252-53), called "The Lord Hath Broken the Staff of the Wicked."

Bibliography:

Perhaps Gilchrist (1880), II, 254 (267).

Russell, *Engravings* (1912), pp. 119-20 (37A).

Collections: George Smith, of Paddockhurst, Sussex; in Gilchrist (1880), II, 276, the sale catalogues of Smith's Blake material are quoted; possibly the above print was "A Frieze of Figures, Coloured," in the July, 1880, sale.

PENCIL DRAWINGS

Agnolo Brunelleschi and the Six-Footed Serpent
(PLATE XXIII)

BRUNELLESCHI stands center, full front, borne down by the monster's weight; his head crushed forward on his right shoulder, as it is engorged by the serpent—"The two heads now became/ One, and two figures blended in one form/ Appear'd, where both were lost." On the left, Dante and Virgil stand attentive. On the right stand, naked, the two other spirits, Puccio Sciancato and Buoso Donati, looking on in horror, one with his back turned and his face profile left. Other snakes lie about the foreground, and on the right a goose-like head emerges from the marsh. In the center background, apparently the "adder all on fire" approaching to destroy and absorb Buoso.

9 11/16 x 12 7/8 inches.

SEE Dante's *Inferno*, Canto XXV. This is one of the seven of his Dante designs that Blake engraved. In the print are minor variations only: e.g., the goose-like head in the right background is, in the print, clearly a snake's. The engraving measures 9 9/16 x 13 3/8 inches. (See Russell, *Engravings*, No. 34, IV. He notes that a pencil study of the central part was in the Richard Johnson sale, April 25, 1912 [712]. See, too, Binyon, *Engraved Designs*, No. 130; and Keynes, *Bibliography*, pp. 182-85.)

Acquired: In New York, December 12, 1916.

Another Version: National Gallery, Melbourne; a water-color drawing (14 1/2 x 20 1/2 inches), from the Linnell Sale, March 15, 1918; reproduced in *Illustrations to the Divine Comedy of Dante by William Blake* (London: National Art Collections Fund, 1922), pl. 51. In Gilchrist (1863), II, 219 (xl); (1880) II, 231 (xl).

Canute

HEAD and shoulders turned slightly to left front, looking up to left. Short, curly beard and coiled mustache; short hair in sculptural curls; three points of his crown seen. The face is youthful. "Canute" at bottom center; and, in right corner, "Dark Hair & Eyes"; "(4)" in left bottom corner, and "9" in right.

10 x 7 5/8 inches.

Bibliography: Gilchrist (1863), II, 245 (52); (1880), II, 260 (43).

Caractacus

HEAD and neck, full-face; large eyes looking up; long, coiling mustache; the hair in stiff, short locks; prominent cheekbones. At the top, "Caractacus"; "(1)" in the bottom left, and "10" in the bottom right, corner.

11 9/16 x 8 inches.

Bibliography: Gilchrist (1863), II, 245 (53); (1880), II, 260 (42).

Queen Eleanor

HEAD and neck slightly to left front, the eyes upturned. Long tresses on each side of her face and neck; three points of her diadem on her hair. "(3)" in the left, "11" in the right bottom corner.

7 3/4 x 6 1/16 inches.

Bibliography: Gilchrist (1863), II, 244 (46); (1880), II, 260 (46).

Joseph and Mary in the Room They Were Seen in

JOSEPH on the left, head and shoulders; his body turned to left front, his head tilted over to the right, the eyes to right front. Youthful face; short, curly hair. In the top left corner, "(8)," and "12" in the bottom.

[33]

Mary stands to the right, nearly half-length, her hands crossed on her bosom, her face turned down to left front, her body slightly to right front. A tress of hair lies on her right shoulder.

Between these drawings is a small, diagrammatic sketch of a room containing a canopied bed. Before it, to the right, Mary stands, full length, in the same pose, but as a child. On the left Joseph, in the same pose but as a little boy, is being led away to the left by an elderly man, presumably his father. On the back, "Joseph and Mary and the room they were seen in."

7 7/8 x 12 3/8 inches.

Exhibited: Tate Gallery, 1913 (70); National Gallery, Edinburgh, 1914 (30); Manchester, Whitworth Institute, 1914 (72)—in each case lent by the Linnell Trustees.

Bibliography: Gilchrist (1863), II, 245 (50); (1880), II, 260 (37).

Old Parr When Young, Viz. Forty

STANDING naked, full length, walking to the front, his right foot forward; the left foot is not drawn. His arms (the hands barely indicated) are extended a little way from the body. His head slightly to left front; curling hair, locks on his shoulders. In the bottom left corner, "Old Parr when young, viz. forty"; in the right corner, "Aug. 1820. W. Blake feċt." The drawing is on the right half of the sketchbook page, which is folded down the center; on the left half, in the right lower corner, up-side down: "Saturday Mr. Pepper called / Vincent / Mr. Sneyd." On the reverse, "Old Parr when young."

11 3/4 x 7 1/4 inches.

Bibliography: Gilchrist (1863), II, 245 (59); (1880), II, 262 (62).
Colleċtions: Perhaps John Linnell; sale, March 15, 1918.

Saladin and the Assassin

SALADIN at the bottom; head and shoulders, profile left, youthful, with long hair parted in the center. At the top the head and torso of a bearded man, in plate armor, lying on his back, the head to the left. At the top, "The Assassin laying dead at the feet of Edwd Ist in the holy land"; at the bottom, "Saladin Blake fecit"; "(6)" in the left, and "13" in the right corner.

12 1/4 x 7 7/8 inches.

Bibliography: Gilchrist (1863), II, 244 (37 and 38); (1880), II, 261 (50 and 54).

Socrates

HEAD and neck, profile left, the eye looking up; retroussé nose; mustache, beard, and whiskers. The forehead modeling strongly marked; curly hair at the back of the cranium. At the bottom, "Socrates"; "(2)" in the left corner, "6" in the right.

On the verso a snouty human profile to the left, and two incomplete human profiles to the left.

12 1/4 x 7 15/16 inches.

Bibliography: Gilchrist (1863), II, 243 (30); (1880), II, 260 (38).

A profile-left head of Socrates, lot 69 in the Aspland Sale, January 27, 1885, is in the Graham Robertson Collection.

Solomon

HEAD and shoulders, profile right; prominent, arched nose, small mustache and lip-beard, and four corkscrew whisker curls at the base of the jaw; three long tresses lie over the nape of his neck. Inscribed at the foot, "SOLOMON"; in left bottom corner, "(5)"; in right bottom corner, "8."

10 3/16 x 8 5/16 inches.

Bibliography: Gilchrist (1863), II, 244 (43); (1880), II, 260 (35).

Uriah and Bathsheba

URIAH on the left, profile left; head and shoulders; thick neck, thick locks of hair, short beard and mustache. In the left lower corner, "Uriah the Husband of Bathsheba" and "7." Bathsheba is on the right, profile left; head and neck; a corkscrew lock of hair lies over her neck. "Bathseba" [i.e., Bathsheba] written in front of her.

8 x 12 7/8 inches.

Bibliography: Gilchrist (1863), II, 244 (40, 41); (1880), II, 259 (33), 260 (34).

Collections: This set of visionary portraits was included in lots 163 and 165 in the Linnell sale, March 15, 1918; lot 165 was bought by Parsons. It appears that three versions of Solomon and two of Canute occurred in these lots. In 1876 George Smith lent a set of "Portraits drawn by Blake from Visions" to the Burlington Fine Arts Club, No. 322.

OIL PAINTINGS

Lot and His Daughters (PLATE XXIV)

L OT, HIS head resting on his left hand, reclines on a bank asleep, center, full front. The daughter on the left, leaning over him, wears a deep-rose-red skirt. The other, on the right, leaning back against the bank, wears a lemon-yellow drapery round her waist. On the ground in front, two cups and a wineskin; center and left background, the interior of a grove; a vine in the right background, and beyond, Sodom in flames against a dark-blue sky. *Signed:* "W. B. inv."

Canvas in oil or tempera, 10 1/4 x 14 7/8 inches.

Exhibited: Burlington Fine Arts Club, 1876 (88), lent by W. B. Scott; Carfax Gallery, London, 1904 (33), lent by J. Annan Bryce; catalogued as having been in the Butts and Aspland collections; Carfax Gallery, London, 1906 (7), lent by J. Annan Bryce.

Bibliography: Gilchrist (1863), II, 223 (111) "[Mr. Rossetti, from Mr. Butts]"; (1880), II, 235 (134) [Butts].

Collections: Thomas Butts; William Rossetti; A. Aspland (?);* William Bell Scott; his sale, April 21, 1885 (186*), bought by Gray.

Acquired: In New York, May 26, 1917.

Blake engraved "Lot's Escape" ("after Rubens"), an illustration to the Protestant's Family Bible (1780). See Keynes, *Bibliography*, p. 225.† A wholly different "Lot and His Daughters" by Blake is in the Auckland Public Library, New Zealand. It represents them seated round a table (see Wright, *Blake*, II, 65, pl. 67).

* No such picture was in the Aspland Sale.
† The engraving suggests that the original of Blake's engraving was Raphael's design in the Loggie. There is no connection with the picture described above.

A Figure from Michelangelo's "Last Judgment"

A STUDY of the figure on the extreme left of the arc of those rising from the dead—the full-front man, with arms raised almost covering his face, who is being pulled up by a crouching figure above him. *Inscribed:* "W Blake 1776."

Paper in oils, 20 1/2 x 12 9/16 inches.

On the back, "William Blake Study for the last Judgment signed and dated 1776, from Mr. Flaxman's collection."

Acquired: In New York, 1916.

IN ADDITION TO THE DRAWINGS AND PAINTINGS
BY WILLIAM BLAKE, THE FOLLOWING DRAWINGS IN
THE HUNTINGTON LIBRARY, NOT BY HIM, HAVE BEEN
ASSOCIATED WITH HIS NAME:

Acis and Galatea, by Henry Pierce Bone (1779-1855)

THE pair seated naked in a shallow cavern in the left corner.
Above, on a plateau, the Cyclops is seated, profile right
against the sky. *Falsely signed:* "W. Blake"; the signature of the
author, "H. P. Bone," partly erased.

Wash, 15 1/2 x 13 1/2 inches.

"*Aimon*," by Henry Fuseli (1741-1825)

INTERIOR of a somber dungeon or tomb. A low doorway in the
right background; on the left, a hero supports a swooning
woman against his right leg. He stands with legs apart, drawing
his sword, looking up to the right at a cloaked figure with spread
arms descending through a shaft of light. Inscribed at the bottom: "ΑΙΜΩΝ" and "Febr. 1800."

On the back a full-length lady standing full front, her head
nearly profile right, the eyes upturned. Her chest is bare, her
cheek rouged, and she wears elaborately curled hair and ruff
collar. A wash of blue behind the head. The drawing from the
waist down is barely indicated in pencil.

Pencil and water color, 17 3/8 x 12 inches.

On the mount, "Aimon" is described as an original study for
Blair's *Grave;* but there seems no connection between this drawing and that poem.

The drawing on the reverse is typical of Fuseli's rather extravagant studies of Regency womanhood. It belongs to the group of drawings of which "The Toilet" (No. 28, Fuseli Exhibition at the E. A. Wilson Gallery, Ryder Street, London, 1935) and "The Fireplace" (No. 21, same exhibition) are well-known examples.

Unidentified Subject, after Fuseli

A HELMETED, naked hero, standing astride a recumbent naked man with his legs drawn up, struggles with an old, long-bearded man, of scaly form, whose navel makes a floral pattern. Round his waist a heavy, iron girdle.

Ink, 8 x 6 3/8 inches.

On the back is written:

"Mit starken sinen handen lief er abbrichen am.

Und vie bi dem barte den alt grisen man";

also, "from the Calcott Sale. W. B. 8 May 05." Sir Augustus Callcott's sales were May 8, 1845, and June 22, 1863. There was an N. J. Calcott Sale, December 16, 1871.

The initials "W. B." might belong to any one of a considerable number of obscure romantic artists exhibiting round about 1800 to 1830. Generally they were so obscure that conjectures as to their identity with the "W. B." connected with this drawing would be futile. The following may, however, be mentioned: William Bagg, W. Bass, W. K. Beacham, William Beechey, W. Bond, W. Boxall, W. Brockedon, W. Bromley, W. H. Brooke, W. W. Browne.

Hercules with the Cretan Bull, after Fuseli

F ULL length, fronting; the legs straddled, the left knee bent; the right arm horizontal, the hand holding the bull's horn; on the right a bow and quiver. *Falsely Signed:* "W. Blake 17.."

—apparently over a thinly penciled "J[?] WB."* On the left a
pencil sketch of a male reclining full front, his right knee raised,
his left arm horizontal. On extreme right an inscription, in dubious Greek characters, reading "ΒΙΗΝ ΗΡα ΚλΚειην Θρασυμεμνον"
(edge torn).

Ink, 11 7/8 x 15 3/4 inches.

On the back are two drawings, in ink, apparently made from
a classic bas-relief: (*a*) A man (Dionysus?) advancing profile
right, a ram accompanying him. In his right hand he bears a
platter. (*b*) Hygieia(?) advancing, profile right, a platter in her
right hand; a snake, wound round her, feeds from it.

Joseph and Potiphar's Wife, after Fuseli

THE FIGURES are racing to the left. Joseph has his right leg
advanced, his right arm stretched horizontally, his left curved
above his head. Potiphar's wife is just seen on the right, clutch-
ing at his back. *Inscribed:* "W. Blake 1797."

Ink, wash, and body color, 4 7/8 x 5 inches.

Amazonian Conflict

A SOLDIER, in classic armor, advancing in the center towards
an Amazon, who kneels three-quarters right, an arrow in
her raised right hand; her face is profile left. A horse in the right
background; a clump of spearmen in the left. *Signed:* perhaps
"A. W." (in monogram), which has been changed to "W. B."

Ink and wash, 5 1/5 x 7 1/2 inches.

"Design for 'America'"

A NAKED youth floats, profile right, on the air. His right arm
extended above his thigh, his left stretched behind him,

* It may be mentioned that William Bromley (1769-1842), painter and engraver, copied the antique.

his head thrown back. Below him to left are two women, leaning out of flames, as it were. Flames in the center and a cliff in the right background.

Water color, 5 3/4 x 11 1/4 inches.

A modern inscription alleges that this is one of the original designs for *America*, published 1793, not engraved. The drawing is of very feeble, amateur quality and resembles none of the engraved drawings in *America*.

Atlas Supporting the Globe

H E STANDS, full face, supporting the globe. On the right, a woman stands profile left. *Falsely signed:* "W. Blake."

Ink, 9 x 5 3/4 inches.

According to Professor A. M. Hind, an Italian sixteenth-century drawing.

Samson Slaying the Philistines

H E STANDS center, profile right. The jawbone in his raised right hand; with his left he seizes the hair of a crouching man on the right. Other figures on the ground about. *Falsely signed:* "W. B."

Ink and sepia, 10 3/8 x 7 3/4 inches.

Apparently an Italian drawing.

The Plates

SATAN CALLING HIS LEGIONS
Paradise Lost

SATAN COMES TO THE GATES OF HELL
Paradise Lost

SATAN COMES TO THE GATES OF HELL
Paradise Lost

CHRIST OFFERS TO REDEEM MAN
Paradise Lost

SATAN'S AND RAPHAEL'S ENTRIES INTO PARADISE
Paradise Lost

SATAN WATCHES ADAM AND EVE
Paradise Lost

RAPHAEL WARNS ADAM AND EVE
Paradise Lost

ROUT OF THE REBEL ANGELS
Paradise Lost

CREATION OF EVE
Paradise Lost

TEMPTATION AND FALL OF EVE
Paradise Lost

JUDGMENT OF ADAM AND EVE
Paradise Lost

MICHAEL FORETELLS THE CRUCIFIXION
Paradise Lost

THE EXPULSION
Paradise Lost

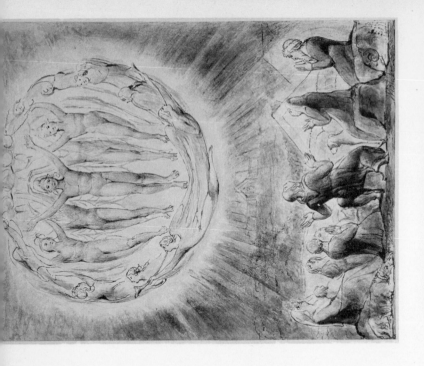

SHEPHERDS AND THE HEAVENLY CHOIR
Nativity

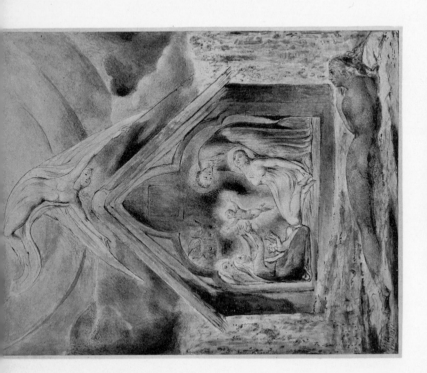

THE DESCENT OF PEACE
Nativity

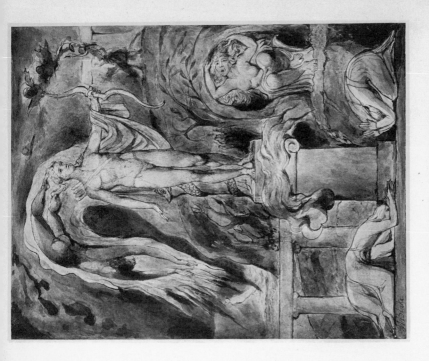

THE OVERTHROW OF APOLLO
Nativity

THE OLD DRAGON
Nativity

THE VIRGIN BLEST
Nativity

THE FLIGHT OF MOLOCH
Nativity

16

COMUS DISGUISED
Comus

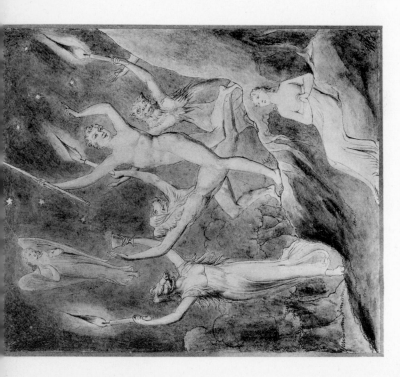

COMUS WITH HIS REVELLERS
Comus

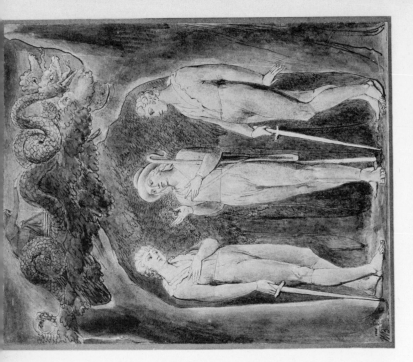

THE BROTHERS IN THE WOOD
Comus

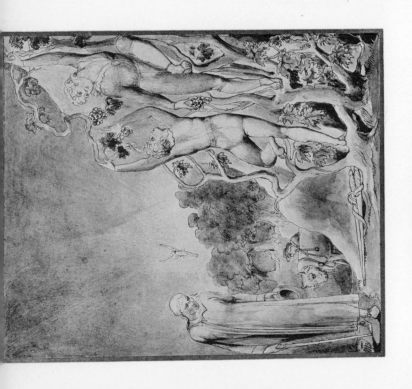

THE BROTHERS PLUCKING GRAPES
Comus

18

THE BROTHERS DRIVING OUT COMUS
Comus

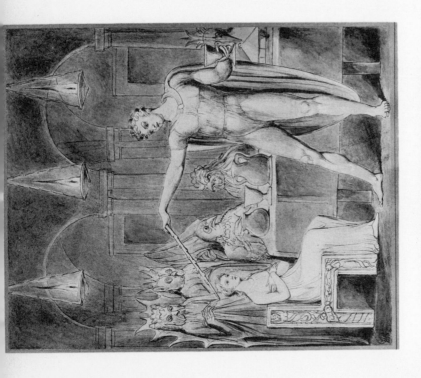

COMUS WITH THE LADY SPELLBOUND
Comus

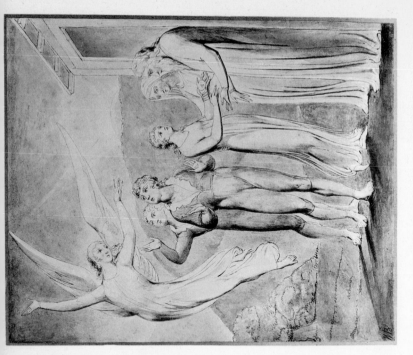

THE LADY RESTORED TO HER PARENTS
Comus

SABRINA DISENCHANTING THE LADY
Comus

THE HIDING OF MOSES

Acts IX c. 6v

CONVERSION OF SAUL

LOT AND HIS DAUGHTERS